Nick Bear

CW00418266

English World

Grammar Practice Book

1

MACMILLAN

A note to teachers, parents and children

Welcome to the *English World* Level 1 Grammar Practice Book.

In this book you will find a variety of activities which practise the grammar points in Pupil's Book 1 and Workbook 1. There are also activities which practise writing skills and phonics/pronunciation. These activities can be used in class or for homework.

There is a unit in the Grammar Practice Book for each unit in the Pupil's Book and the Workbook. There are three pages in each unit:

- **Page 1 of each unit** practises the **main grammar point** of the unit.
- **Page 2 of each unit** practises the **Grammar in conversation** point.
- **Page 3 of each unit** has a **Grammar Street** activity, which practises the grammar points from pages 1 and 2; and a **Writing skills** activity which practises the writing from the Workbook Writing skills page.

The **Review pages** practise the grammar from the previous three units. Each grammar activity in the Review units has a score out of 5. This gives a total score of 20. The children write their score for the Review pages in a box on the page. They can assess their level of achievement by reading the comments in the **Score Box**.

The phonics and spelling section of each unit in the Pupil's Book is practised at the end of this book.

When all the activities in each unit are complete, the Grammar Practice Book will be a useful reference and revision aid for the children. The series of Grammar Practice Books builds up into a complete record of the grammar in *English World* .

The children can keep their Grammar Practice Books and use them for reference in later levels of *English World.* In this way, they develop good study skills and make an important step to becoming independent learners.

Contents

Unit 1

It is a car.
It is white.

Is it a boat? Yes.
Is it black? No.

1 Read and colour.

Is it a dog?

No, it isn't. It's a fish.

Is it yellow?

Yes.

Is it a cat?

Yes, it is.

Is it white?

No, it's brown.

2 Write. Use the words in the box.

Is it	It is	~~No~~ 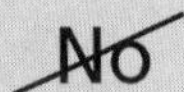

It is	Is it	Yes

1 Is it a kitten? No.

2 ________ a dog.

3 ________ a teddy? Yes.

4 ________ a dog? No.

5 Is it a cat? ________.

6 ________ a cat.

1 Circle the correct words.

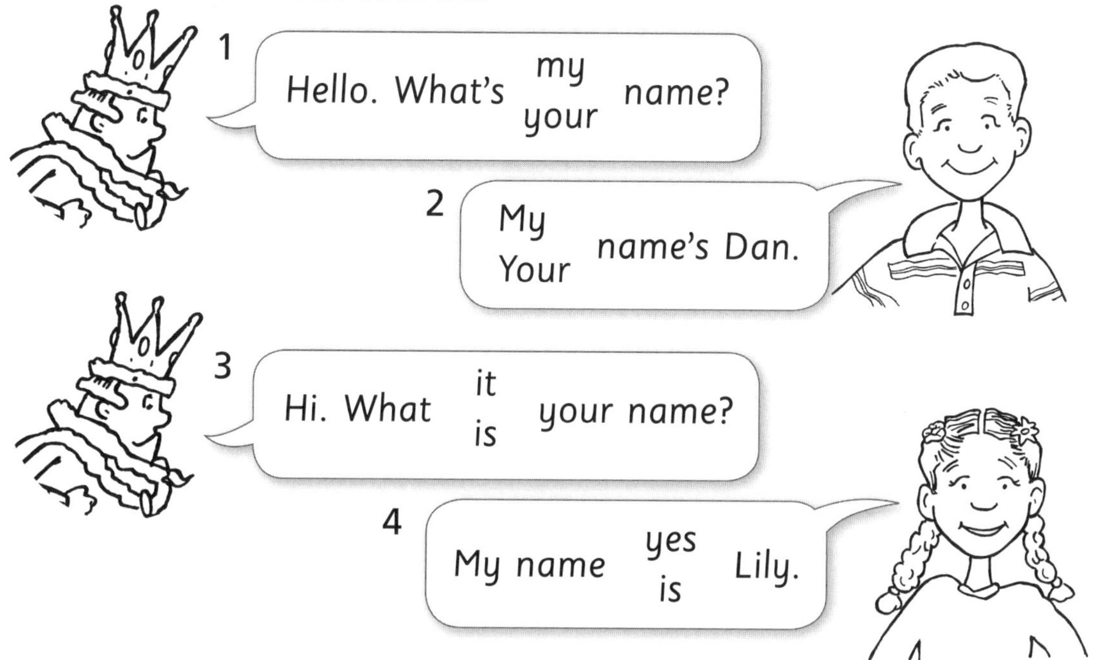

2 Write. Use the words in the box.

Bella	your	is	My

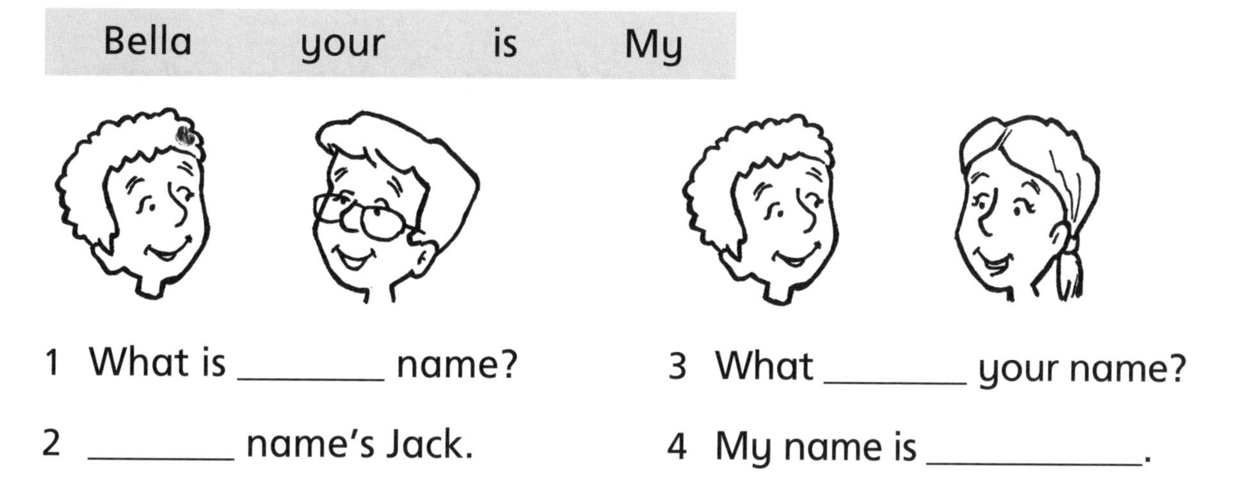

1 What is ________ name?

2 ________ name's Jack.

3 What ________ your name?

4 My name is ___________.

1 Write.

Writing skills

2 Match the letters.

h m i

M I H

3 Write the capital letters from Exercise 2. Add the full stops.

Unit 2

Is it red? Yes, it is.
Is it a car? No, it is not.
It is not a car.
It is a van.

1 Match and colour.

1
It's a bag.
Is it red?
Yes, it is.

2
It's a pencil.
Is it yellow?
No, it isn't. It's blue.

3
It isn't a bag.
It isn't a pencil.
It's brown.

2 Write. Use the words in the box.

Is it	Yes	it is	It is	No	not

1 _______ a rabbit.

2 It is _______ a kitten.

3 _______ a dog? No, it is not.

4 Is it a kitten? Yes, _______

5 Is it white ? _______, it is not.

6 Is it black ? _______, it is.

1 Match.

1 What is it? — b It is a train.
2 Is it a train?
3 Is it a car?

a No, it is not.
b It is a train.
c Yes, it is.

4 What is it?
5 Is it a boat?
6 Is it a car?

d Yes, it is.
e No, it is not.
f It is a boat.

1 b 2 ____ 3 ____ 4 ____ 5 ____ 6 ____

2 Write.

1  It is a bag.

2 

It is ______ a pen.

3  ______ is it? It is a rubber.

4  What is ______? It is a crayon.

5 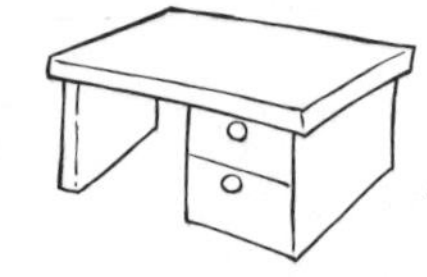 Is it a desk? Yes, it ______

6  ______ it a crayon? No, it is not.

1 Write.

Grammar Street

Writing skills

2 Write the capital letters.

1 n N

2 i ____

3 y ____

3 Write the capital letters from Exercise 2. Write the full stops.

Is it a train?

1 ____es, it is

What is it?

2 ____t's a boat

Is it a taxi?

3 ____o, it isn't

Unit 3

It is an umbrella.

It is a white bike.

It is not a black car.

1 Choose.

1 It is a / an apple.

2 It is a / an brown taxi.

3 It is a / an orange.

4 It is a / an grey umbrella.

5 It is / is not a bike.

2 Write.

1 It ________ ________ umbrella.

2 It ________ ________ ________ car.

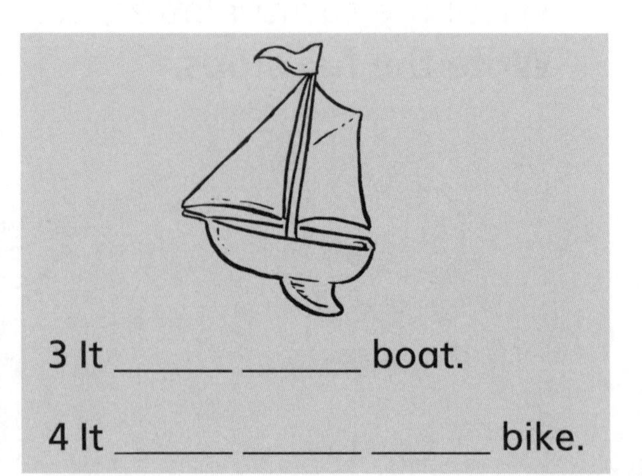

3 It ________ ________ boat.

4 It ________ ________ ________ bike.

1 Match.

A

1 Good — a Jolly
2 very — b morning
3 Mr — c well

B

4 Good — a you?
5 How are — b afternoon
6 I'm fine, — c thank you

1 b 2 ____ 3 ____ 4 ____ 5 ____ 6 ____

2 Write. Use the answers to Exercise 1.

1 Write.

Writing skills

2 Read and write. Use the words in the boxes.

It is a taxi.

yellow

It is a lorry.

green

1 It is a yellow taxi.

3 It is ____________________

It is a boat.

purple

It is an umbrella.

orange

2 It is ____________________

4 It is ____________________

Review 1

It is a car. / It is not a bike. It is red. / It is not blue

1 Write.

book bag

1 It is a book.
It is not a bag.

umbrella bike

3 ______________
____

kitten dog

2 It is a kitten.
____

pencil pen

4 ______________
____

Score ___ /5

Is it a bike? Yes, it is. / No, it isn't.

2 Write questions. Match the answers.

1 Is it a kitten?
2 ______ ball?
3 ______ rabbit?
4 ______ book?
5 ______ car?
6 ______ boat?

Yes, it is.

No, it isn't.

Score ___ /5

a / an

3 Write *a* or *an*.

1 Is it __a__ car?
2 Is it ____ umbrella?
3 No, it isn't. It's ____ apple.
4 Is it ____ orange?
5 Is it ____ nut?
6 No, it isn't. It's ____ egg.

Score ___ /5

4 Make sentences.

1 it / purple / bag It is a purple bag.
2 it / green / ball ________________
3 it / orange / book ________________
4 it / brown / dog ________________
5 it / yellow / taxi ________________
6 it / blue / boat ________________

Score ___ /5

My score is __________.

10–13

14–17

18–20

Unit 4

He is happy.
She is not happy.

Is he happy? Yes, he is.
Is she happy? No, she is not.

1 Match.

1 She is
2 She isn't
3 Is he sad?
4 Is he happy?
5 Is she happy?
6 Is she sad?

a No, he isn't.
b Yes, she is.
c No, she isn't.
d happy.
e sad.
f Yes, he is.

1 d 2 ___ 3 ___ 4 ___ 5 ___ 6 ___

2 Write.

1 He is big.
2 ________ is small.
3 He is ________ small.
4 She ________ not big.
5 Is ________ big? Yes, he is.
6 ________ she big? No, she isn't.

big small

1 Circle the correct words.

2 Write. Use the words in the box.

Yes	she	are	No	I	He	is	am

1 She ________ fast.

2 Is she fast? Yes, ________ is.

3 Am ________ slow? Yes, you ________

4 I ________ big.

5 ________ is small.

6 Is he small? ________, he is.

7 Is she small? ________, she isn't.

1 Write.

Writing skills

2 Choose and write.

S s

1 She is Miss __ilver.

S s

2 She isn't __ad.

B b

3 He is __iffo.

B b

4 He isn't __ig.

Unit 5

There is one cake.

How many sweets are there?

There are two sweets.

1 Choose.

Picture A

1 There is one dogs / dog.

2 There are / is one cat.

3 There is one / three rabbit

Picture B

4 There is / are four cats.

5 There are two / one dogs.

6 There are three rabbit. / rabbits.

2 Look at picture B. Choose and write.

are There many How four there one

1 How ________ chairs are there? There is one chair.

2 ________ many balloons are there? ________ are three balloons.

3 How many hats ________ there? There is ________ hat.

4 How many cats are ________? There are ________ cats.

1 Match.

1 Is there one boat?

2 Are there two boats?

3 Is there one car?

4 Are there two cars?

5 Is there one plane?

6 Are there three planes?

Yes

No

2 Write. Use the words in the box.

How	Is	there	many	three	Are

1 __________ there two lollipops? No.

2 __________ there one lollipop? Yes.

3 Are __________ six sweets? Yes.

4 Are there __________ cakes? Yes.

5 __________ many balloons are there? There are two balloons.

6 How __________ ice creams are there? There are four ice creams.

1 Write.

Writing skills

2 Write ? or .

1 There are two cakes__

2 There is one lollipop__

3 Is there one cake__ Yes, there is__

4 Are there two cakes__ Yes, there are__

5 How many sweets are there__ There are five__

Unit 6

What are they?
They are frogs.

1 Look and write a, b, c, d or e.

a  b c  d e 

1 What are they? They are flowers. __d__

2 What is it? It is a flower. ____

3 We're sad. ____

4 I'm sad. ____

5 We're happy. ____

2 Write. Use the words in the box.

They	are	We	is	It

1 What ______ they?

2 ________ are frogs.

3 What ______ it?

4 ______ is a bird.

5 ________ are sad.

1 Match the questions and answers.

1 e 2 ___ 3 ___ 4 ___ 5 ___

2 Write.

1 Write.

Grammar Street

Writing skills

2 Write the sentences.

trees. big are They

big It cake. a is

is frog. It green a

1 They are big trees. 2 ________________ 3 ________________

are They cars. red

a sad He clown. is

4 ________________ 5 ________________

Review 2

He is happy. / I am happy. / We are happy.

1 Write.

1 He __is__ slow.

2 I ______ fast.

3 We ______ sad.

4 I ______ happy.

5 She ______ pretty.

6 He ______ thin.

Score ___ /5

Is he happy?	Yes, he is.	Am I happy?	Yes, you are.
Is he sad?	No, he isn't.	Am I sad?	No, you aren't.

2 Write questions.

1 she / sad / ? __Is she sad__? Yes, she is.

2 she / happy / ? ______________? No, she isn't.

3 I / slow/ ? ______________? No, you aren't.

4 I / fast / ? ______________? Yes, you are.

5 it / fast / ? ______________? No, it isn't.

6 it / slow / ? ______________? Yes, it is.

Score ___ /5

There is one ruler. / There are six pens.
Is there one sweet? Yes.
How many sweets are there? Three

3 Write *is* or *are*.

1 There ___is___ one lemon.
2 There ______ two apples.
3 ______ there one egg? Yes.
4 How many oranges ______ there? There are two.
5 There ______ three pencils.
6 There ______ one book.

Score ___ /5

What are they? They are frogs.
How old are you? I am six. / We are seven.

4 Write questions and answers.

1 ______________________? They are sweets.
2 What are they? ______________________
3 ______________________? I am eight.
4 How old are you? ______________________
5 What are they? ______________________
6 How old are you? ______________________

Score ___ /5

My score is __________. 10–13 14–17 18–20

Unit 7

Where is the mouse?

It is in the box.

It is on the box.

It is under the box.

They are in the hat.

1 Read and draw.

1 The flower is in the jug.

2 The balloons are under the teddy.

3 The apples are in the box.

4 The lemons are in the bag.

5 The ruler is on the lemons.

6 The rubber is on the umbrella.

2 Write.

1 teddy/box The teddy is in the box.

2 lemons/chair ______________________

3 balloons/umbrella ______________________

4 flower/bag ______________________

Where is my book? It is in the bag.
Where are my pens? They are not in the bag.

1 Find and match.

1 Where is my bag?
2 Where are my books?
3 Where are my balloons?
4 Where is my umbrella?

a They're in the living room.
b It's in the bedroom.
c They are not in the castle.
d It's on the table.

1 d 2 ___ 3 ___ 4 ___

2 Write.

1 Where are the fish? They ______ in the living room.
2 Where ______ the birds? ________ are ____ the garden.
3 Where ____ the present? It's ____ the kitchen.
4 ________ is the kitten? ____ is ____ the bathroom.
5 Where ____ the dog? It ____ on the stairs.

1 Write.

Writing skills

2 Read and write *he*, *she*, *it* or *they*.

1 Biffo is on the chair.

He is on the chair.

2 Miss Silver is in the rocket.

______ is in the rocket.

3 King Tub and Princess Bella are in the garden.

________ are in the garden.

4 Pirate Jack is on the ship.

______ is on the ship.

5 The chairs are in the living room.

________ are in the living room.

6 My bag is in my bedroom.

______ is in my bedroom.

Unit 8

I have got a brother.

I have not got a sister.

Have you got a dog?

Yes, I have.

Have you got a cat?

No, I haven't.

1 Choose.

1 I have got / have not got an apple

2 I have / have not got a melon.

3 I have got / have not got a lemon.

4 You have / Have you got an orange?

5 Yes, I have. / haven't.

6 Have you got / got you a banana?

7 Yes, / No, I haven't.

2 Write.

1 I ________ got a car.

2 I have ________ got a boat.

3 I have not ________ a plane.

4 ________ you got a rocket?

5 ________, I haven't.

6 Have you ________ a castle?

7 Yes, I ________

This is my brother.
Who is this?
She is my sister.
Is this your father?
Yes.
1 Match.
1 This is my sister.
2 This is my family.
3 Who is this?
He's my brother.
4 Is this your mother?
Yes.
5 Who is this?
She's my grandmother.
6 Is this your grandfather?
Yes.
a
b
c
d
e
f
1 e 2 ___ 3 ___ 4 ___ 5 ___ 6 ___
2 Write.
1 Who is this?
He is my brother.
2 ______ this your father?
Yes.
Who is this?
3 She ____ my grandmother.
4 Is ______ your sister?
Yes.
5 ______ is this?
He is my grandfather.

1 Write.

Grammar Street

Writing skills

2 Write. Use *and*.

1 He is happy. She is happy.

He is happy and she is happy.

2 There is an apple. There are two oranges.

____

3 He has got a boat. He has got a car.

____

Unit 9

He has got a plane.
Has he got a car?
No, he hasn't.

She has not got a plane.
Has she got a car?
Yes, she has.

1 Match.

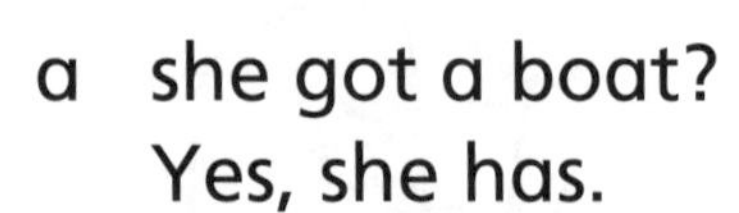

1 I

2 He

3 She has

4 Has

5 I've got

a she got a boat? Yes, she has.

b a boat.

c has got a boat.

d have got a boat.

e got a boat.

1 d   2 ___   3 ___   4 ___   5 ___

2 Write.

1 He has ______ a castle.

2 She has ______ got a castle.

3 She ______ got a rocket.

4 He ______ not got a rocket.

5 ______ he got a crown? Yes, he ______

6 ______ she ______ a crown? No, she hasn't.

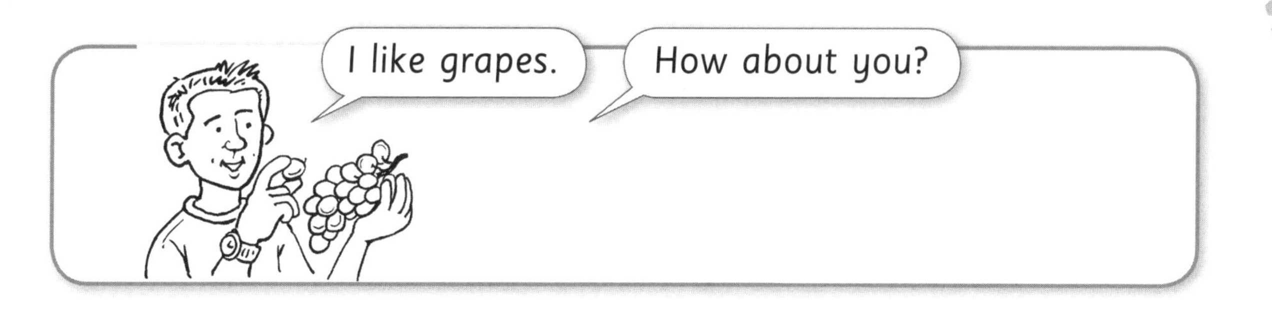

1 Follow the lines. Cross out the wrong sentences.

2 Write.

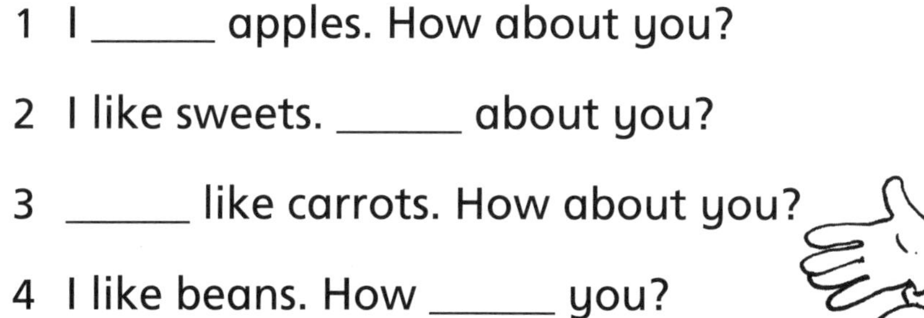

1 I ______ apples. How about you?

2 I like sweets. ______ about you?

3 ______ like carrots. How about you?

4 I like beans. How ______ you?

5 I like oranges. How about ______?

1 Write.

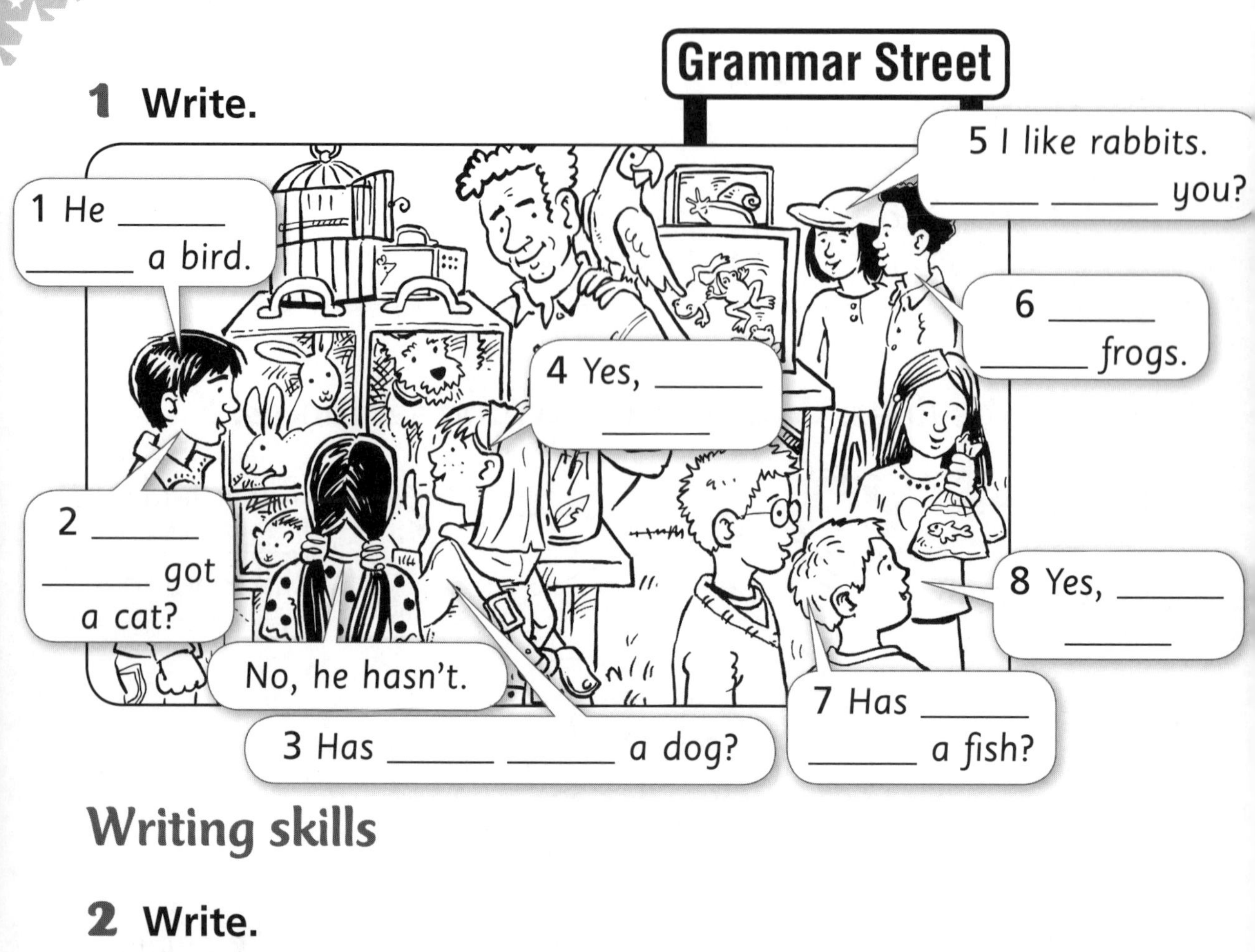

Writing skills

2 Write.

1 Miss Silver has got a rocket.
Her rocket is big.
Miss Silver has got a big rocket.

2 King Tub has got a crown.
His crown is new.
____

3 Pirate Jack has got a hat.
His hat is old.
____

4 Biffo has got shoes.
His shoes are red.
____

Review 3

My pen is in my bag.

1 Write *in*, *on* or *under*.

1 My pen is under my bag.
2 My books are ________ my bag.
3 My ruler is ________ my bag.
4 My cap is ________ my bag.
5 My apple is ________ my bag.
6 My banana is ________ my bag.

Score ___ /5

Where is my book?
It is in / on / under the bag.

Where are my pens?
They are in / on / under the box.

2 Write questions and answers.

1 Where is my book? It is in the living room.
2 Where ______ my cards? ________ are in the kitchen.
3 ________ are my balloons? They are ______ the living room.
4 Where ____ my dog? It ____ in the garden.
5 ________ is my cat? It is ____ the bedroom.
6 Where ____ my umbrella? It is in the bathroom.

Score ___ /5

I have got a ... Have you got a ...? Yes, I have. / No, I haven't.
He has got a ... Has she got a ...? Yes, she has. / No, she hasn't.

3 Write *have, have not, has* or *has not*.

1 I have got a dog.

2 ________ you got a car?
Yes, I ________.

3 He ________ got a dog.

4 I ________ got a boat.

5 He ________ got a boat.

6 ________ he got a car?
No, he ________.

Score ___ /5

Who is this? This is my ....
I like ... How about you?

4 Write in the correct order.

1 this? Who is — Who is this?

2 my This father. is ________

3 like apples. I ________

4 about How you ? ________

5 is This mother. my ________

6 sweets. I like ________

Score ___ /5

My score is ________.

10–13

14–17

18–20

Unit 10

The frog can jump.
The frog cannot fly.

Can it jump? Yes, it can.
Can it fly? No, it can't.

1 Look. Circle *can* or *can't*.

1 The bird can / cannot fly.

3 Can / Can't the girl draw? Yes, she can. / can't.

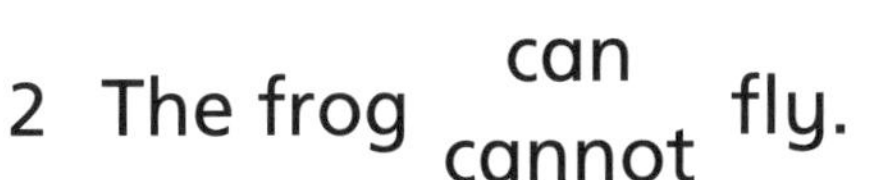

2 The frog can / cannot fly.

4 Can / Can't the boy sing? No, he can. / can't.

2 Look again. Write. Use the words in the box.

it	No	can	cannot	fly

1 The girl ______ draw.

2 Can the bird fly?
Yes, ____ can.

3 Can the frog ______?
____, it can't.

4 The boy ______________ sing.

Can we cross? Yes, you can.
Stop! Look! Listen! Wait!

1 Match.

1 Listen!

2 Sit down!

3 Cross!

4 Stand up!

5 Look!

6 Stop!

1 b   2 ___   3 ___   4 ___   5 ___   6 ___

2 Write. Use the words in the box.

look	road	~~we~~	can	~~OK.~~

1 Can we cross the ________?

No. Stop!

OK.

2 Then ________!

OK.

Then listen!

3 ____OK____.

4 All right. Now you ________ go.

1 Write.

Writing skills

2 Circle the words.

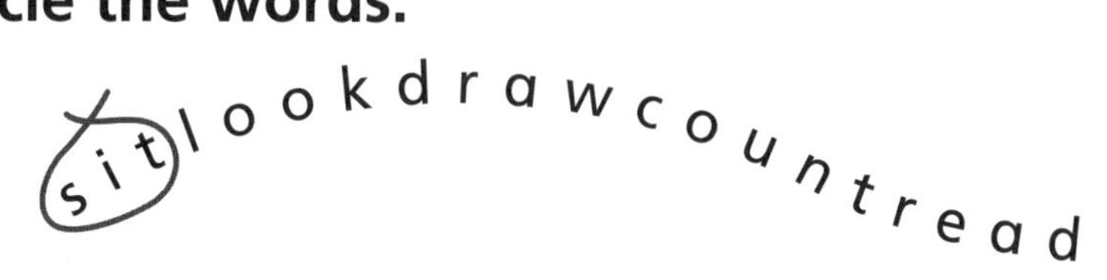

3 Write. Use the words in Exercise 2.

1 ________ at the rocket.

2 The frog cannot ________

3 Can the bird ________? No, it can't.

4 ________ on the chair.

5 ________ the numbers.

Unit 11

I am drawing.

You are singing.

1 Match.

1 I am reading. ____

2 I am writing. ____

3 I am drawing. ____

a

b

c

4 You are standing. ____

5 You are listening. ____

6 You are jumping. ____

d e f

2 Write. Use the words in the box.

reading I am You jumping are

1 I am ____________.

2 You are ____________.

3 ____ am standing.

4 ____ are listening.

5 I ____ drawing.

6 You ______ singing

What is the weather like?
It is cloudy.
Is it cold? Yes, it is

1 Read. Match with Picture a or Picture b.

1 What's the weather like?
It's sunny. ___a___

2 Is it windy?
Yes, it is. ______

3 What's the weather like?
It's cold. ______

4 Is it hot?
Yes, it is. ______

2 Write. Use the words in the box.

Is	is	like	No	hot	it

1 What's the weather ______?

2 It's ______

3 Is ______ raining?

4 ______, it isn't.

5 ______ it sunny?

6 Yes it ______

1 Write.

Writing skills

2 Write. Use the question words in the box.

what where how many

1 ____________ is the monkey? It is on the chair.

2 ____________ colour is the monkey? It is black.

3 ____________ ____________ monkeys are there? There is one.

4 ____________ are the flowers? They are under the chair.

5 ____________ colour are the flowers? They are white.

6 ____________ ____________ flowers are there? There are five.

Unit 12

1 Choose and circle.

1 He is / am reading.

2 I am / is jumping.

3 They am / are pointing.

4 It is / are flying.

5 She am / is singing.

6 We are / is talking.

2 Write. Use these verbs.

stand   eat   listen   talk

1 She is talking.

2 They ______________.

3 He ______________.

4 They ______________.

She is walking quickly.

1 Choose.

1 He is walking quickly. / loudly.

2 She is talking quietly. / loudly.

3 I am walking slowly. / quickly.

4 They are singing loudly. / quietly.

5 We are reading quietly. / loudly.

6 It is flying quickly. / slowly.

2 Write in the correct order. Match.

1 slowly. walking They are

They are walking slowly.

2 quickly. is He walking

____

3 am I loudly talking.

____

4 talking is She quietly.

____

a 

b 

c 

d 

1 c 2 ___ 3 ___ 4 ___

1 Write. Use these verbs.

Grammar Street

jump
walk
draw
~~read~~
talk
play

1 He _is_ _reading._

2 It ________ ____________

3 ________ are ________

4 We ________ ________.

5 She ________ ________ quietly.

6 ________ are ________ slowly.

Writing skills

2 Complete. Use the words in the boxes.

1 | a book | He | _He_ is reading _a book._

2 | They | the road | ____________ are crossing ____________

3 | sweets | We | ____________ are eating ____________

4 | You | a cat | ____________ are drawing ____________

5 | a kite | Biffo | ____________ is holding ____________

6 | Miss Silver | a present | ____________ is opening ____________

Review 4

It can jump.
It cannot fly.

Can it jump? Yes, it can.
Can it fly? No, it cannot.

1 Write *can* or *cannot*.

1 The bird can fly.

2 The frog ________ fly.

3 The frog _____ jump.

4 _____ the frog talk?
No, it ________

5 _____ the cat walk?
Yes, it _____

6 _____ the dog sing?
No, it ________

Stop! Look!

Score ___ /5

2 Read the words in the box. Write.

Listen	Write	~~Stop~~	Look	Cross	Read

1 Stop!

2 ________!

3 ________!

4 ________!

5 ________!

6 ________!

Score ___ /5

What is the weather like ? It is cloudy.
Is it cold ? Yes, it is. / No, it isn't.

3 Write questions and answers.

1 What's the weather like? It's sunny.

2 Is it hot? ______, __________.

3 __________ cold? No, it isn't.

4 What's __________ like? It's cold.

5 ______________windy? Yes, it is.

6 ______________hot? No, it isn't.

Score ___ /5

I am flying./You are singing./He is eating./We are reading./
They are jumping./She is talking loudly.

4 Write.

1 reading. I am ______I am reading.______

2 She running quickly. is ______________________

3 They quietly. are talking ______________________

4 jumping. are We ______________________

5 He loudly. laughing is ______________________

6 You slowly. walking are ______________________

Score ___ /5

My score is __________.

10–13

14–17

18–20

Phonics and spelling

Review 1 Units 1–3

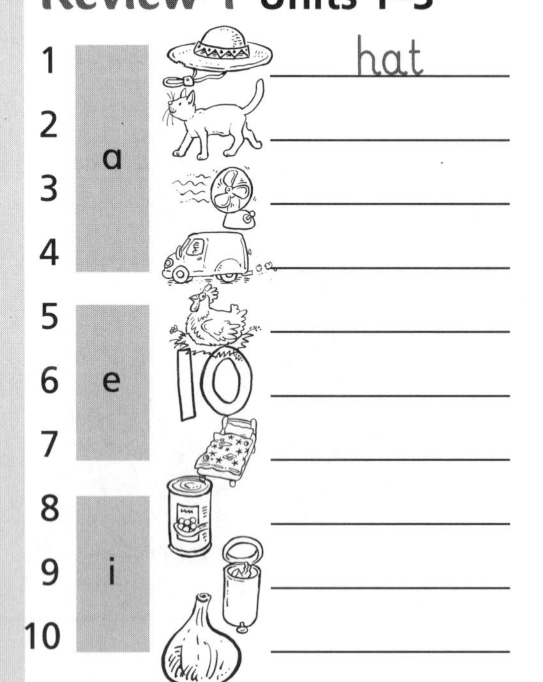

1	a	hat
2		
3		
4		
5	e	
6		
7		
8	i	
9		
10		

Review 2 Units 4–6

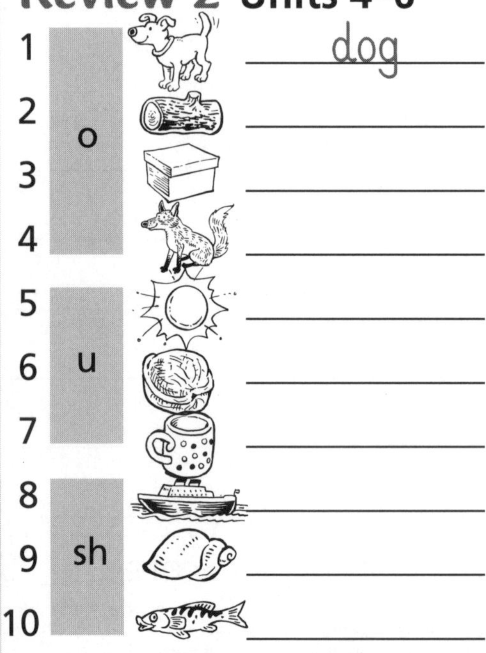

1	o	dog
2		
3		
4		
5	u	
6		
7		
8	sh	
9		
10		

Review 3 Units 7–9

1	ch	chip
2		
3		
4		
5	th	
6		
7	htye	
8	th	
9		
10	3	

Review 4 Units 10–12

1	ing	king
2		
3		
4		
5	ll	
6		
7		
8	ck	
9		
10		